KISSING
BRIDGES

THE COLOSSUS

HEGEN PETERSEN

Foreword by Richard Sanders Allen

THE STEPHEN GREENE PRESS, Brattleboro, Vermont · 1965

About This Book

THE INGREDIENTS of any bridge include common sense, a grasp of engineering principles, many hours of planning (financial as well as structural), perhaps an eye for beauty. Certainly in the case of the covered bridge as we know it in North America these requisites are present, plus an extraordinary degree of craftsmanship.

Hence the timber bridge has a widening appeal today: to the enthusiast and "collector," to the amateur (and sometimes the professional) engineer and architect, to the artist and to the tourist. To all of these a roofed span appeals to the historian who lurks, I suspect, in all of us: for the covered bridge—a large and sometimes engagingly gawky relic of the last century—gives a glimpse into the past, tells us a little bit more about how our forefathers lived and what they thought about.

So the purpose of *Kissing Bridges* is to salute the more than 1500 covered bridges still standing on this continent, to help locate them, and to tell and to show something about how covered bridges were built—and when and why.

There is nothing "new" here. All the material has been mined from the researches of more scholarly bridge buffs than I. To these real students, several of whom are mentioned under "If You Want to Dig Deeper" in the back of this book, the author wishes to express a debt of gratitude. I am especially beholden to the prime authority in this field, Richard Sanders Allen, for massive help with facts and illustrations. Most of the pictorial material here is from his collections.

I also want to thank Paul L. Atkinson, the staff of the Brattleboro Free Public Library, J. Stott Dawson, Harold F. Eastman, Janet Greene, Mrs. Karl K. Knight, Mrs. Orrin H. Lincoln, Leo Litwin, Mrs. J. Waide Price, Claude Remaly, and Mrs. Vera H. Wagner, for generous help.

And I am obliged to the following photographers, artists and other picture sources for material on the pages indicated: Eugene R. Bock (t. 3 b. 21, t. 38), H. Lee Hull (b. 3), McNaught Syndicate, Inc. (4), Ky. Dept of Public Info. (t. 5), Smithsonian Institution (b. 5, t. 18, 27), Howard L. Humes (6, b. 39), George Daly (7, 10, 28, 35), E. H. Royce (9, 11), Glenn A. Wagner (12), N. Y. State Historical Assn. (14), Mass. Dept. of Commerce (16), Robert MacLean (17), Alvin W. Holmes (19), Carter Co. C of C (20), *Warren Tribune-Chronicle* (t. 21), Oregon Highway Dept. (22), Kramer Adams, Weyerhaeuser Timber Co. (23), C. P. Goddard Coll. (b. 24, 31), Wills Coll. (26), New-York Historical Soc. (29), Va. Highway Dept. (b. 32), New Brunswick Travel Bur. (33), Lucy G. Loekle (34), Sidney Pepe (36) Howard C. Bogue (b. 38), N. J. Council (t. 39), N. C. Dept. of Conserv. & Devel. (t. 40), D. T. Caldwell, Jr. (b. 40), W. Va. Indust. & Public. Comm. (43), Wisc. Conserv. Dept. (44), Ontario Dept. Travel & Public. (45), Newspaper Enterprise Assn. (b. 46). H.P.

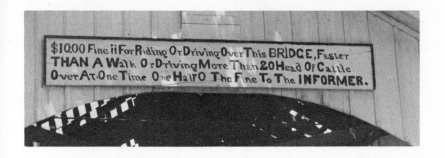

Foreword

CHAMPIONS of the old and the picturesque are hard at work in many corners of the United States, seeking to preserve as many of America's covered wooden bridges as is practicable. These spans are tangible reminders of the work of our forefathers, and are part of our national heritage.

Like the nation's railroads, canals and shipping, the stories behind these well-loved landmarks have attracted devotees from all walks of life. To the true enthusiast, no facet of covered bridge lore is too obscure to collect and correlate with previously gained knowledge, or to be recorded and shared with others.

We have had the covered bridge learnedly dissected in engineering treatises, extolled nostalgically in poetry, detailed in local histories with copious footnotes, and treated with a combination of all these approaches. Somewhere in between the first awareness of the existence of these structures and dedicated partisanship in their preservation, are those with just plain curiosity about covered bridges.

It is to provide enlightenment and enjoyment for a great number of people who have a casual, but nonetheless sincere, interest that Mr. Petersen's book has been written.

Round Lake, New York   RICHARD SANDERS ALLEN
February 1965

Cows complement view of old Huntington, Vt., bridge.

Trees to Spare and Yankee Know-How

MAYBE you've never seen one before. You're driving along a quiet road almost anywhere in the U.S.A. and eastern Canada, and you approach what looks like a slender barn built across a stream.

Its sides may be the color once called buttermilk red, or perhaps white, or the silver-gray that can't be matched except by years of weathering. You come nearer: it's open-ended, and your road leads through its heavily timbered length. What is it?

It is one of the 1500-odd covered bridges still standing in this continent, and it harks back to the days when American genius used wood to preview the soaring steel spans of today.

The American covered bridge, a curiosity to the tourist, was a commonplace of the last century. As pioneer settlements gave way to more conventional communities, fords and ferries proved inadequate and were replaced by timber bridges, often privately financed and paid for later by toll charges. Thousands of bridges were put up after 1800, first along the Atlantic seaboard, then later through the South, West and North—in fact throughout most of forested America.

As these timber spans are in turn being displaced, they seem to become the nostalgic symbols of a rural America that has also all but gone. They recall half-forgotten memories of loose floorboards slapping under the wheels of a surrey, or of the advantages bridge rafters offered to young acrobats, or of the musty aroma, unique to the covered bridge, compounded of weathered wood and, until a generation ago, horse.

Shoes, circuses and corsets were once advertised in this Switzer, Ky., bridge.

The sight of some back-road covered bridge today reminds us of the ghost stories and legends of gory crimes that tingled the scalp of many a small boy who walked its gloomy length at dusk.

Or perhaps revives that favorite among "funny" covered bridge yarns: the rube teamster heading into Pittsburgh from a small town in Ohio who, on reaching a covered bridge over the Allegheny, saw that the entrance was large enough for his load but considered the hole at the other end entirely too small—and headed back home again.

"Kissing bridges" they were widely known as at one time, for their dark interiors proved ideal for what a later generation was to refer to as spooning. "Wishing bridges" they were, too, for everybody knows that a wish made in a covered bridge comes true.

The signs on old covered bridges, some still found today, are especially evocative: stern warnings not to drive faster than a walk; statements of toll charges taking you back to the days when a penny really bought something; colorful circus bills, and advertisements for such wondrous products as Dr. Flint's Powders, Kendall's Spavin Cure, Kickapoo Indian Oil, Battle-axe Plug Tobacco.

And for the historian, these bridges have often played a role in battle. Confederate Lt. Bennett Young, in the northernmost engagement of the Civil War, set the Sheldon, Vt., bridge on fire to evade capture as he galloped toward the nearby Canadian border after his daredevil raid on St. Albans. The ill-fated John Brown captured and for a while held the S-shaped bridge over the Potomac River during his attack on Harpers Ferry, then Virginia. And now-forgotten bridges were fought over, destroyed and rebuilt again throughout the South during the Civil War.

Massive stone piers support this Red River crossing near Port Royal, Tenn.

Old Fish House Bridge at Northampton, N.Y., typifies Burr-type construction.

The American covered bridge, product of lush forests and Yankee ingenuity, represents a brief but all-important step in the evolution of bridge building, from the first crude log crossing in prehistory to the Verrazano-Narrows masterpiece over the entrance to New York harbor, now the longest bridge in the world.

Bridges with roofs were in use long before their appearance in North America. The 14th-century Ponte Vecchio in Florence, and even older Chinese crossings, were covered—and stand today—even though these stone structures were roofed for reasons quite different from the one used in covering our great wooden bridges of the last century.

But in Switzerland and other regions of Europe where trees are, or were, plentiful, more than 200 covered timber spans are still in use—with several dating back to the 14th century.

How much the American covered bridge owes to its European antecedents is not known. Perhaps they all had a common ancestry. Certainly the work of Timothy Palmer, the Newburyport, Mass., inventor and housewright who built the first known American covered bridge in 1805, bears a striking resemblance to the truss designs recorded by Andrea Palladio, the Italian whose pioneering *Treatise on Architecture* was translated into English in 1742.

Palmer's 1805 structure, named The Permanent Bridge, was built across the Schuylkill in Philadelphia. Other important covered bridges were built in this area, so the reputation of Vermont, or at least New England, as the heartland

WHAT A TRUSS IS

A truss, according to the dictionary, is an assemblage of members (such as beams, bars, rods and the like) so combined as to form a rigid framework—that is, one which cannot be deformed by the application of exterior force without deforming one or more of its members.

Properly designed, the helpful dictionary goes on, a truss should be in the form of a triangle, or a combination of triangles, because this is the only polygon whose shape cannot alter without changing the length of its sides.

 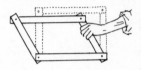

The Kingpost (shown below), long employed in barns and other structures here and abroad, is such a combination of triangles, and is perhaps the simplest form of truss.

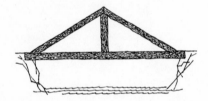

Palladian designs, and the Palmer and Burr bridges deriving from them, involved trusswork which combined an Arch with the Kingpost. More sophisticated trusswork, developed by Wernwag, Town, Long, Howe and others (see diagrams, page 10), evolved from these prototypes.

The simple stringer, or beam, bridge—for example, a couple of logs laid across a narrow brook—does not require trusswork. But trusses are needed 1) when the space to be bridged is wider than the available timbers are long (and intermediate piers, for one reason or another, are unfeasible); or 2) when the load to be carried is too much for the strength of the timbers.

The great achievement of the early American builders was in spanning sizable obstacles with wooden bridges of lengths never before attempted, and which for decades—and at a time when bridges were vital to the growth of our country—safely supported substantial traffic loads.

RATES OF
TOLL.

Every Foot Passenger, - - - - - - **3**

Every head of live Sheep, Hogs or Calves, - - - **1**$\frac{1}{2}$

Every head of Horned Cattle, - - - - - **9**

Every Horse, Jack, Mule or Ox, whether led or drove, - **9**

Every Horse or Mule and rider, - - - - **12**$\frac{1}{2}$

Every two wheel Pleasure Carriage, drawn by one Horse, } **18**$\frac{3}{4}$
Jack or Mule,
and SIX CENTS for every additional Horse, Jack or Mule.

Every four wheel Pleasure Carriage, the body whereof is sup- } **25**
ported by springs or thorough-braces, drawn by one Horse, Jack or Mule,
and TWELVE AND A HALF CENTS for every additional Horse, Jack or Mule.

Every Pleasure Wagon, drawn by one Horse, Jack or Mule, **25**
and TWELVE AND A HALF CENTS for every additional Horse, Jack or Mule.

Every Stage Wagon, drawn by one Horse, Jack or Mule, **18**$\frac{3}{4}$
and SIX AND A QUARTER CENTS for every additional 3d or 4th Horse, Jack or Mule.

Every Stage Wagon, drawn by five Horses, Jacks or Mules, **37**
and TWENTY-FIVE CENTS for every further additional Horse, Jack or Mule.

Every Freight or Burthen Wagon, drawn by one Horse, } **12**$\frac{1}{2}$
Jack, Mule or Ox,
and SIX CENTS for every additional 3d, 4th or 5th Horse, Jack, Mule or Ox.
And for every further additional Horse, Jack, Mule or Ox, TWENTY-FIVE CENTS.

Every Cart or other two wheel Carriage of burthen, drawn } **12**$\frac{1}{2}$
by one Horse, Jack, Mule or Ox,
and SIX AND A QUARTER CENTS for every additional Horse, Jack, Mule or Ox.

Every Sleigh or Sled, of any description, drawn by one } **12**$\frac{1}{2}$
Horse, Jack, Mule or Ox,
and SIX AND A QUARTER CENTS for every additional Horse, Jack, Mule or Ox.

Fine of One Dollar,

For any person or persons crossing the Mohawk Bridge on Horse
Back or in a Carriage or Sleigh of any description, to travel faster than on a walk, or
For any person to cross said Bridge with Horses, Jacks, Mules
or Oxen, consisting of more than Ten in one Drove, or to cross with Loaded Carriages or Sleighs drawn by
more than two beasts, at a less distance than 30 feet, each from the other, or
For any person or persons with Carriage or Carriages, Sleigh or
Sleighs of any description, or with any kind of Beasts to take the left hand passage.
5000 Dollars Fine for attempting to injure or destroy said Bridge.

of the American covered bridge is only partially earned. Today there are more covered bridges standing in the Keystone State than in all of New England.

However the earliest designers and builders, and the most influential ones, were Yankees. Palmer, as we have seen, came down from north of Boston to build Philadelphia's hopefully named Permanent Bridge in 1805. And Theodore Burr, a millwright's son from Torringford, Conn., modified and enlarged upon the Palladian plans, and his design was eventually extended to all parts of the country.

Burr's famous patent, taken out in 1805, combined arch and kingpost (see truss diagrams on page 10) and was first used in the long-lived 800-foot Hudson River crossing at Waterford, N.Y., which stood for 105 years. He erected dozens of his spans in New York and New Jersey before moving to Pennsylvania— where he went bankrupt in attempting to build simultaneously five huge bridges across the wide Susquehanna.

Burr, certainly one of the greatest of American bridge builders, died penniless, his place of burial unknown today. But friends and subcontractors took over where he left off and firmly established the Burr-type truss in Pennsylvania, Maryland and the Virginias. His name lives on in the Midwest where it was often uncapitalized and corrupted into "bur" or "bir." On the West Coast any span with an arch was known as a "Burr." Crossings are still being built in New Brunswick—"Bhurr bridges," these are called—to the formula of the Connecticut millwright's son.

Interior of bridge near Enosburg, Vt., shows detail of Town's lattice mode.

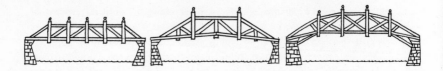

Three bridge truss designs described by Andrea Palladio.

Palmer, Burr and their men shaped the big timbers and ancillary planks with the crudest of tools: the broadaxe, the adze, the wooden plane; once shaped, the truss members were assembled flat on the ground at the site to be spanned, joined by mortises and tenons, or pinned, as the case might be. Then one whole side of a bridge, and later the other, was pulled out over falsework (later removed) and lowered onto its abutments. Floor, roof, portals and other refinements were added later. Until the late 1800's, only the most prominent and important bridges were painted.

It took considerable in manpower and know-how to put together the big timbers of the Palmer and Burr structures. There was obvious need for a substantial bridge that could be built by an ordinary carpenter's gang.

In 1820 little, red-headed Ithiel Town, native of Thompson, Conn., foresaw this need, and developed and patented an entirely new kind of truss which he called his "lattice mode." This was simply a series of diagonally crisscrossed planks attached to one another at each intersection by hardwood pegs called treenails (pronounced to rhyme with funnels).

Even though an awful lot of holes had to be augered, and pegs driven, in a Town lattice—approximately 2590 for every 100 feet of bridge length—it was a comparatively easy structure to build, and therefore lent itself to mass production. "It could be built by the mile and cut off by the yard," its proponents claimed.

Town licensed his truss design (at $1 per running foot) to builders throughout the country, and probably more were built on his plan than any other in New England and the South.

Herbert W. Congdon, in a book devoted mainly to Vermont bridges, has pointed out that the early American bridge builders could not make calculations in advance from definite knowledge of material strengths and similar technical matters, as our engineers do today. Rather, they were ingenious men of little schooling: they built by rules of thumb, learned through experience.

In 1830 Stephen H. Long, a New Hampshire-born explorer and U.S. Army engineer, devised the first American bridge truss into which a few mathematical

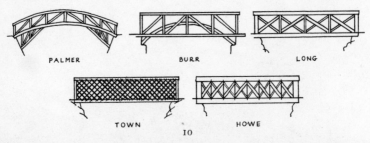

calculations entered. His patented design was in effect a continuous series of overlapping kingpost trusses, or giant boxed X's. Highly popular for about 10 years, they are still occasionally to be seen, especially in Ohio bridges.

The Long bridge was also popular with railroad companies. But a young farmer and inventor from Spencer, Mass., named William Howe thought he could improve on the Long trusses put up by the Western RR near his home. For the upright wooden posts in the Long plan, he substituted iron rods equipped with nuts and turnbuckles—and so not only strengthened the bridges but also allowed the truss members to be more readily adjusted if they got out of kilter from heavy loads.

Thus William Howe introduced the material—iron—which not only started the greatest spurt in building wooden covered bridges, but which also was to lead to the end of wood as the principal material in American bridges. But before iron—and later steel and concrete—took over entirely, Howe's prefabricated patented truss was used in several thousand bridges from Maine to California. Many survive today.

The honor roll of great American bridge builders is a long one. It includes designers and innovators such as German-born Lewis Wernwag, who was responsible for the bold and beautiful Colossus of Fairmount at Philadelphia, and

Neat Hectorville Bridge spans south branch of Trout River near Montgomery, Vt.

Oldest covered RR bridge in U.S. (1877) is at Bennington, N.H.

the oddly shaped Harpers Ferry bridge made famous by *John Brown's Body;* Willis Pratt, who patented a reverse Howe-type truss favored for some years by railroad builders; Squire Whipple, the schoolteacher and student of bridge construction who introduced the "trapezoid truss" but who is better known for his theories and his iron bridges.

And there were others, such as Nicholas Powers of Vermont, who drew the plans for a big bridge over the Susquehanna River during his lunch hour; the giant span at North Blenheim, N.Y., and at least four bridges in Rutland County, Vt., were put up by this colorful builder. Or Lemuel Chenoweth of West Virginia, who won the contract for bridges on the Staunton & Parkersburg Turnpike in 1850 by suspending his fragile-looking little truss model between two chairs and walking its length as part of his sales pitch to a Virginia Board of Public Works.

These men and many more like them played a vital part in bridging America. But it was these five that led the way: Palmer and Burr, with their rediscovery and adaptation of the Palladian truss and arch; Town and Long, who put substantial bridge design within the reach of ordinary carpenters, and Howe, who brought a standard plan and prefabrication to a high degree of perfection.

WHY COVERED?

George Washington, despite what folktales say, never laid eyes on a covered bridge.

For until 1805 no bridge in America could boast a roof. In that year, when Timothy Palmer was building his Permanent Bridge over the Schuylkill, a Philadelphia jurist named Richard Peters suggested that the bridge would last a good deal longer if its principal parts were covered to prevent rot. This suggestion was followed, and The Permanent Bridge became the first covered bridge in America.

Judge Peters's idea was a good one. While wood will long survive when fully submerged in water, it deteriorates quickly when alternately wet and dried. An uncovered wooden bridge has a life expectancy of from 10 to 15 years; an uncovered wooden bridge treated with a chemical preservative has a somewhat longer life. But a properly roofed bridge should last almost indefinitely.

As an Eastern seaboard bridge builder once put it: "Our bridges were covered, my dear Sir, for the same reason that belles wore hoop skirts and crinolines—to protect the structural beauty that is seldom seen, but nevertheless appreciated."

In the 19th century sometimes just the trusses (that is, the supporting sides) were tightly boxed in with weatherboarding, and the roadway was left uncovered. The Haverhill, Mass., RR bridge, below, is an example of this type of protection. But a regular roof over the whole thing, using less lumber and allowing easier inspection for weaknesses, proved more satisfactory in the long run.

Springtime view of Burkeville Bridge over South River at Conway, Mass.

over to the State of Alabama; the state had given it to the federal government for preservation as a national historic site. While all this was going on, though, the bridge itself was given no repairs. It silently rotted, and finally collapsed in July 1963.

Nevertheless, what's surprising is not that covered bridges are falling so fast, but that so many still remain. In the map on the opposite page an attempt has been made to give the general location and number of the 1500 or so standing bridges on the continent.

They exist today all over forested America: on the Atlantic seaboard—where they originated—and in the South, Canada, the Midwest and on the West Coast. We will outline briefly here some regional differences in covered bridges. (There's a more detailed state-by-state rundown in the section headed "Make Them Your Own," starting p. 35.)

THE NORTHEAST

The two earliest designers and builders of American covered bridges were New Englanders—though they erected their spans in Pennsylvania and New York.

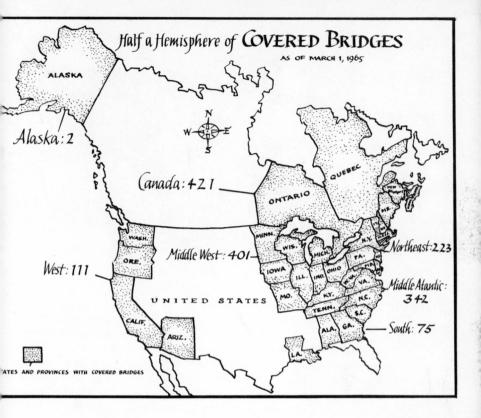

Half a Hemisphere of **COVERED BRIDGES**
AS OF MARCH 1, 1965

ALASKA

Alaska: 2

Canada: 421

QUEBEC
ONTARIO

Northeast: 223

WASH.
ORE.

Middle West: 401

West: 111

UNITED STATES

Middle Atlantic: 342

CALIF.
ARIZ.

South: 75

STATES AND PROVINCES WITH COVERED BRIDGES

Also Yankees were the three most prolific inventor-promoters of the framed wooden trusses which followed the work of the true pioneers.

Therefore it was only natural that throughout the Northeast and Middle Atlantic area there would be a consistency of bridge design, using the arch-truss inspired by Palmer and Burr, the lattice of Town, or the boxed X's of Long and Howe. Examples of designs attributable to these five men (with the exception of Palmer) exist today, and may be visited over a twelve-state area.

The majority of New England's sturdy covered bridges are of the Town cross-hatched lattice "mode," with a scattering of Howe and Long varieties. In Pennsylvania the Burr-arch type and its derivations are almost completely dominant; this influence is also notable in adjacent Maryland and the Virginias.

The student of covered bridges can usually make quick identification of a Pennsylvania covered span: not only because of its arched trusses, but by the greater use of stone, with carefully dressed abutments, piers, and wide parapets leading up to the well-proportioned portals.

THE SOUTH

Ithiel Town actually built very few bridges on his patented design and, oddly enough, his first construction jobs were in North Carolina. They soon caught on, however, and the older crossings in the Carolinas, Alabama and Georgia all

Glass Bridge near La Grange, Ga., was work of ex-slave Horace King.

reflect the influence of the spry little go-getter and his lattice.

There are Howe trusses as well, introduced in the South by the railroads, then adapted for nearby highway bridges. In the piney barrens of Mississippi some novel abutments were built: cylindrical concrete caissons in several instances, and brick piers in at least one case. Not one of these Mississippi bridges survives.

One of the best builders in the Alabama-Georgia area was a freed slave, Horace King, a lattice adherent who sired a couple of generations of covered bridge builders and repairers. None of his bridges is standing today, but the plan he advocated became popular and is still evident.

Most Deep South bridges, unhappily, are notable today for the state of disrepair into which they have been allowed to fall. Typically shrouded in honeysuckle and morning-glory, they present a picturesque appearance. But except for a very few preserved as a result of local interest, most are doomed through apathy.

Concrete piles kept typical Deep South bridge (near Aberdeen, Miss.) out of water's reach.

Full interior ceilings, corbels, keystoned portals and arcaded sidewalks feature Kennedy brothers' Vine Street Bridge in Shelbyville, Ind.

The well-kept Doe River Bridge at Elizabethton, Tenn., dates from 1882.

THE MIDDLE WEST

Here the picture is less gloomy. The Midwest has always been noted for the variety of its bridge types, with the Town lattice imported from New England, the Burr truss from Pennsylvania, and Lewis Wernwag's arch emulated in valleys adjoining the National Pike. Trusses of the Long type were introduced by the Colonel's agents throughout the region, and especially by his brother in southern Indiana.

In addition, a number of new bridge designs originated in the Midwest. There were bold experiments with reverse arches and other innovations which, surprisingly, usually worked out in practice. Robert W. Smith patented a lattice-type truss which was widely used in Ohio in the latter part of the 19th century; the Partridge truss gained favor in Ohio and northern Indiana, and the Brown truss (invented in Buffalo, N.Y.) proved popular in Michigan.

Notable in both Indiana and Ohio were the covered timber canal aqueducts built by small companies which couldn't afford to build their conduits entirely of stone. One such survives (see illust. to right) in Metamora, Ind.

Particularly active in Indiana were two bridge-building families: the Danielses and the Kennedys. The elder Daniels came from New York State, built on Long's plan in Ohio, then settled in Rockville, Ind. His son Joseph brought the business to full flower and was responsible for dozens of Burr-arch bridges in the area.

On the eastern side of the state the Kennedy family, originally from North Carolina, built big and sturdy Burr-type bridges, often attractively embellished, during the 1880's on down to 1917-20. (Indiana builders had the helpful habit of inscribing their names and other useful data on the portals of many of their structures.)

Iowa's spans, with their lattice variations and their flat roofs, were often mounted on piles or iron caissons. The Illinois bridges are also to be found high above the sluggish rivers on stiltlike underpinnings. Their construction usually reflects the geographic origins of the people who settled near by.

Most of the CB's are built on the Howe principle, with such modifications as slanted roofs added over the portals to give extra snow protection.

Roofed timber bridges in both Quebec and New Brunswick are fast disappearing, although some effort has recently been made, especially in the Maritime province, to preserve them.

ALASKA

A dozen or so CB's were built in Alaska, more or less based on the utilitarian Oregon principle, by government agencies opening up new areas in the 1920's. Only two survive.

Although the American covered bridge properly belongs to the 19th century, not a few, as we have seen, were built in this one. And the past twenty years, thanks to an ever-growing interest in these structures, have produced fine new spans that are timbered and roofed in the traditional manner. The Bissell Bridge outside Charlemont, Mass., is a case in point, as are even more recent Bay State crossings in Sheffield and Pepperell.

Privately built structures, such as the cozy High Mowing Farm bridge in Wilmington, Vt., are put up in some part of the country almost every year. Footbridges have been especially popular in recent years. Arizona's lone covered span is a footbridge built in the Phoenix Zoo so that desert-bred youths, according to a zoo official, will know what covered bridges look like.

It used to be said that "few there are who like a covered bridge until it is gone." This is fortunately no longer entirely true. Since World War II individuals and groups in many parts of the country have become interested in preserving and renovating the older bridges, and several societies have been formed to make the work more effective. (We'll have more to say about the work of these societies in a later section.)

In addition to the purely nostalgic appeal of covered bridges, it is being increasingly realized that these big handcrafted relics—which do a space-age job with old-fashioned integrity—can teach lessons in history, geography and engineering. Moreover, they provide wonderful subjects for the artist or photographer, and they act like magnets for tourist dollars.

State boards of development and historic sites, chambers of commerce and museums are all alive today to these values. As a result bridges not native to their present sites are to be found preserved in Brown County, Ind., Dearborn, Mich., Shelburne, Vt., Sturbridge, Mass., and elsewhere.

The case for preservation is well put by Leo Litwin, for many years president of the National Society for the Preservation of Covered Bridges:

"Keen public interest is the keynote to the successful preservation of the covered bridges which are left today. Interested enthusiasts, genuinely and sincerely fond of these old spans, realize that once those still in existence are allowed to disintegrate and disappear from our national scene, the United States will suffer a loss to our national heritage that can never be replaced."

Where's the Difference?

BECAUSE OF the attrition in covered bridges these days, the superlatives ascribed by the true fan to his favorite—the highest, the oldest, the longest single span, etc.—must be changed almost as often as track-and-field records. As the result of fire or high water or neglect or "progress," the second-oldest yesterday may become the oldest today, and tomorrow itself may be gone.

We'll try to spot some current record-holders for you later on. Meanwhile there is no question but that covered bridges not only are distinctive from standardized concrete crossings, but they also vary among themselves. No two, in fact, are exactly alike.

First, their sites differ, and thus dictate whether the bridges are a single span from bank to bank, or are multispan structures partially supported by one or more piers rising from the riverbed. Wide but sluggish streams allowed many piers; swift currents or ones likely to be choked with ice floes required that the bridge rely on the strength of its truss alone to carry the roadway to the other side. Indeed, it was the size and fury of America's rivers that demanded wooden bridges that were engineering masterpieces.

Then, their abutments are different. These shore foundations upon which the bridge rests are made of dressed stone, rubble masonry, wood, concrete, even brick. And, as is especially notable in Pennsylvania's crossings, they may have graceful parapets to guide traffic into and out of the bridge.

Or they may be double barreled—that is, have two lanes with a divider down the midline. Double-barreled covered bridges were a concession to heavy traffic, and definitely big time.

Some have walkways for pedestrians—either inside or, supported by bracing,

Storm.

Battered painting shows ancient Johnstown, Pa., aqueduct.

on the outside of the truss; in which case the roof is built farther out on that side to protect those traveling on foot.

Sometimes the siding is solid, but often it is left off under the eaves to allow bands of light into the dusky wooden tunnel from high on either side. Long spans have openings at eye level, or even actual windows. The sheathing itself is applied horizontally; or vertically, and once in a while with battens to cover the seams. One popular bridge in Maine has shingle siding (see illustration p. 38).

Portals can overhang or rise straight, and come in all sizes and shapes, from the severely simple to really ornate entrances like those of the well-remembered old Union Bridge in Pittsburgh. Roofs vary in pitch and overhang; sometimes they are built flat, like the ones in Madison County, Iowa.

And like old London Bridge of the nursery rhyme, that tumbled-down crossing that once carried the equivalent of a town along its roadway, the American covered bridge has housed more than dust and antique signs in its interior. Mailboxes, toilets, stoves, prize-fight rings, wash lines, podiums for musicians or soap-box orators, tables for church suppers, and shrines—all have been recorded within the shelter of its weathered boards.

Few of the oddest covered bridges have survived, and it is a sad fact that most CB's standing today are not as interesting as many of the departed ones. This is

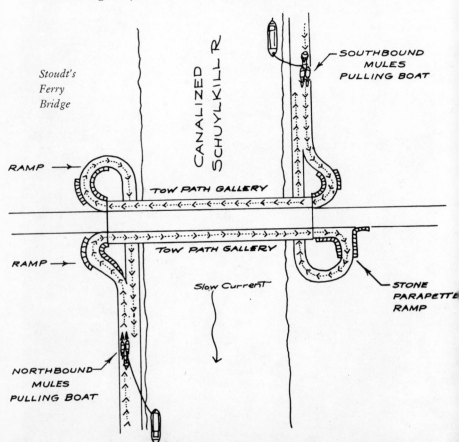

because the designers and builders naturally were called on to make their most spectacular efforts at the big crossings; these bridges were the first to yield to expanding traffic demands.

For instance, take the 1857 Stoudt's Ferry Bridge north of Reading, Penna. This 238-foot single span not only bore a highway across the Schuylkill; since the river was canalized at that point, and the towpath shifted banks, the bridge had to be built in such a way that the mules towing the boats in two directions could cross without fouling the lines. The accompanying diagram shows the ingenious solution, anticipating by a century today's cloverleaf traffic intersections.

Over the Potomac at Georgetown, Ithiel Town erected an aqueduct which was rebuilt after the Civil War (on the more modern Howe truss plan) to become a rarity among CB's: a covered canal with roadway on top. The jets of surplus water spurting from its sides led one humorist of the day to refer to it as "the punctured dragon of the Potomac."

Covered aqueducts of more modest size were not unusual. One in Johnstown, Penna., is shown on p. 27; a number were built in Indiana and Ohio during the early part of this century.

Another bridge of notable eccentricity was Theodore Burr's crossing of the Mohawk at Schenectady. Its floor timbers hung from huge overhead beams by laminated cables of flat plank: it was actually an all-wood suspension bridge. The sagging trusses gave the structure the look of melted chocolate when seen in profile.

We have already spoken of the old Harpers Ferry bridge featured in John Brown's raid. Another odd crossing was the covered Y-shaped bridge at Zanes-

Historic Harpers Ferry Bridge, W. Va., played Civil War role.

The famed covered Y Bridge at Zanesville, Ohio, spanned the Muskingum and Licking rivers from 1832 to 1901.

ville, Ohio. Four Y bridges have graced this location since 1814, their peculiar plan made necessary by the confluence of two rivers. The bridge in use from 1832 to 1901 was a fully roofed truss.

Its modern counterpart has the same distinctive shape, so Zanesville residents, in response to a traveler's inquiry as to how to get to Columbus, nearly 60 miles to the west, could reply:

"Go to the middle of the bridge and turn left"—directions which certainly must be unique in the U.S.A.

The bridge designs of Palladio, the Italian architect, and some of the Burr successors provided for the roadway to follow the rise of the arch, making the bridge higher in the middle than the ends. A handsome humpback bridge, well worth a visit, still stands west of Covington, Va., today. (See picture next page.)

Some real giants went up in the early days of American bridge building, many-piered affairs that could hardly have been expected to survive. The all-time record, as far as is known today, belongs to the first Columbia-Wrightsville (Penna.) span, built by Connecticut-born Jonathan Walcott in 1812. It was 5690 feet in length, hopscotching across the broad Susquehanna River on 28 piers.

Since the collapse of the huge Tallapoosa River bridge in Alabama in 1963, the longest CB in the United States today is probably at Cornish-Windsor (N.H.-Vt.) where James F. Tasker spanned the Connecticut River in 1866. This centenarian is of lattice type, has two clear spans ("clear span" being the distance between the face of one abutment or pier, and the next) of more than 203 feet each.

This Connecticut River crossing from Cornish, N.H., to Windsor, Vt., is probably longest in U.S. The photo dates from the toll bridge era, shows "guillotine" toll gate.

This second Columbia-Wrightsville, Pa., covered bridge was world's longest.

The longest covered bridge on the continent, however, is indisputably the bridge across the St. John River at Hartland in New Brunswick. It consists of seven spans of the Howe type for a total length of 1282 feet. The monster dates from 1899, and is the town's greatest tourist attraction.

One of the longest single-span bridges—over 340 feet, with no intermediate pier for additional support—and one of the loveliest (see title page picture), was built in 1812 by Lewis Wernwag across the Schuylkill. No doubt reminding antiquarians of the enormous statue that once straddled the harbor at Rhodes, it was named The Colossus. It succumbed to fire in 1838.

The distinction of the longest single-spanner existing today belongs to Old Blenheim, with which Nicholas Powers bridged Schoharie Creek at North Blenheim, N.Y., in 1854. Its modified Long truss has a clear span of 210 feet and is hung from a unique single center arch which also forms the divider between two lanes. This double-barreled landmark received national publicity when its 100th anniversary was marked by a community celebration.

A close runner-up is the West's oldest surviving covered crossing. Its 208-foot clear span carries traffic over the South Fork of the Yuba River at Bridgeport, Calif.

Some of the shortest bridges on record are privately owned, and usually of recent construction. Falling into this category are the 22-foot High Mowing Farm Bridge, built in 1949 in Wilmington, Vt., and the 16½-foot Smith's Sawmill bridge near Manoa, Penna. Arizona's lone CB, the 36-foot footbridge at the Phoenix Zoo, can probably claim to be the shortest in the West.

The oldest covered bridges in the United States are approximately 130 to 135 years old. Exactly *which* is now the oldest is difficult to pinpoint, but we will mention a few whose dates of construction seem reasonably well documented.

A number of covered bridges with authenticated dates of 1832-37 stand in the Pennsylvania counties of Adams, Berks and Bucks. Humpback Bridge near

Arch was purposely built into famed Humpback Bridge (Covington, Va.) in 1835.

The Howe-truss Hartland Bridge, in New Brunswick, is now continent's longest.

Covington, Va., was built in 1835, and the long bridge over the Ammonoosuc River at Bath, N.H., dates from 1832.

In Vermont stands the Old Arch Bridge at Waitsfield, built in 1833. And the Pulp Mill Bridge over Otter Creek just north of Middlebury is supposed to have been put up in the 1820's (which may well be).

Another valid contender for age honors is the venerable span over Shadow

Brook at Hyde Hall south of East Springfield, N.Y. This one was erected as part of the George Clark country estate sometime between 1815-30.

All these are bridges of the Burr-arch type or its derivatives. There are also a few Town lattice covered bridges which were built not too many years after the type was invented and patented in 1820. These include the Upper Bridge over the Housatonic River at Sheffield, Mass. (1835), Gage Bridge near Bellows Falls, Vt. (1835), West Swanzey, N.H. (1832), and Woodsville, N.H. (1829).

After 1830, railroad companies were busy for half a century erecting covered bridges. These were, characteristically, high-shouldered (for engine clearance) and narrow, built usually on the Howe plan with the adjustable iron verticals giving them added stability. Always vulnerable to fire from engine sparks, they were sometimes lined inside with sheet metal, and often whitewashed.

The 25 or so remaining railroad covered bridges are to be found today in New Hampshire and Vermont in the East, and Oregon and Washington in the West. The oldest survivor is at Bennington, N.H., and the longest is near Monroe, Wash.

Until recent years two housed timber bridges at Troy, N.Y., and near Seattle, Wash., carried highways *over* railroads, rather than the trains themselves over bodies of water.

The only known CB built expressly for trolley cars once stood in Hampden, Maine. However one across the Merrimack River at Bow Junction, N.H., had gantleted track for both steam and electric rail traffic.

These are just a few of the more unusual or famous covered bridges. But it should be noted that most wooden-truss spans are neither particularly long, nor especially old. They are just everyday covered bridges, carrying a minor highway over some river. If you're a real bridge buff, though, you enjoy these plain-faced specimens every bit as much as their more glamorous cousins.

Massive bracing shows in this underside view of Old Blenheim (N.Y.) Bridge.

Make Them Your Own

THE "COLLECTOR" of covered bridges is unlike most other buffs in that he cannot in the ordinary course of things buy, beg, swap for, or otherwise acquire the subjects of his collection.

Nevertheless, he can hunt for and visit them, paint them, photograph them, dig into their history. He can collect postcards, drawings, paintings, Christmas cards, early stereoscopic views—in fact all kinds of pictures or models of bridges.

But since covered spans still exist in more than half the 50 states of the Union and in four Canadian provinces, he may decide as the better part of valor to confine his attentions to all the bridges in his own area before touring farther afield.

The bridges are almost all to be found on back roads, away from through-ways and interstates, often on unpaved roads off numbered state routes. There-fore if he sticks to major arteries he could drive over much of North America without seeing even one of the 1500 or so covered bridges that remain today. They are usually reachable, though, with a bit of mapwork after leaving a main thoroughfare, and a sign such as "10,000 lbs. safe load limit" can well be a passport to adventure with no danger involved to life, limb, or to an auto-mobile's paint or running gear.

With this in mind, we offer the following information on covered-bridge states and Canadian provinces. More specific location and a capsule description of each known standing covered bridge is given in *World Guide to Covered Bridges,* listed on p. 48. State highway departments are also helpful.

The bridge totals given below do not, for the most part, include small garden-type, trussless, or nonfunctional bridges. These are especially ephemeral.

Nonetheless a cautionary note is in order: covered bridges are being destroyed, and to a lesser extent, built, almost every day. The following was as accurate as we could make it at time of writing. However portions may already be dated: so check with all possible sources of information before starting a long collecting tour.

THE UNITED STATES

Alabama. Has approximately 23 standing bridges (second highest total in the South), confined to the northern portion of the state, with concentration in Blount and Cullman counties. Neglect and apathy are making heavy inroads.

Alaska. Of the dozen or so built here by the government in the 1920's, only two remain: one near Hyder on the British Columbia border, and the other on remote—you'll need a boat or plane to see it—Afognak Island, where the span served a now-deserted cannery.

Arizona. Sole CB in the state is a footbridge in the Phoenix Zoo which dates from 1962.

California. Some 12 CB's remain, all in the northern section above Santa Cruz. Bridgeport and Knight's Ferry bridges in the Mother Lode country are outstanding.

Connecticut. Just five remain of more than 60 built in this state: at West Cornwall, Bull's Bridge (between Kent and Gaylordsville) and East Hampton; plus private spans east of Portland and near Newtown.

Delaware. All three remaining cross Red Clay Creek in the northern part of the state near Wooddale and Ashland.

District of Columbia. No CB's remain in the nation's capital, but the Smithsonian's Museum of History and Technology (where eventually some 60 models will show the evolution of all bridge development from earliest times to the present) will interest most readers of this book.

Tallapoosa River, Ala., crossing, once nation's longest, fell from neglect in 1963.

Unionville, Conn., bridge (1859-1922) in holiday garb.

Georgia. Less than 30 bridges exist, mainly in the northern part of the state. This is the highest state total in the South, but the figure is falling fast. The southernmost covered bridges in the United States still stand in Early County. Write Tourist Division, Georgia Department of Industry & Trade (100 State Capitol, Atlanta) for a brochure picturing and locating each bridge.

English Creek Bridge, east of Durham, Iowa, is less well known than its Madison County cousins.

This Claysville, Ky., span was a replacement for one destroyed in the Civil War.

Illinois. Nine bridges remain, generally in the western half of the state. Hamilton Bridge, once part of a long Mississippi River crossing, and Wolf Bridge, over Spoon River near Galesburg, are outstanding. See *Covered Bridges in Illinois, Iowa and Wisconsin,* listed on p. 47, or write the Division of Highways (State Office Building, Springfield) for up-to-date information.

Indiana. Close to 140 still standing, a wide variety of building styles, and keen public interest make Indiana one of the leading CB states. Parke County's yearly festival, in which the county's 30 or so bridges play a prime role, is worth a visit in October. Write Parke County Tourist Information Center (Rockville) for details. The covered wooden aqueduct at Metamora, near Brookville, is unique in the U.S.

Maine's Robyville Bridge is notable for shingling on top, sides and portals.

One of New Jersey's two covered bridges, Sergeantsville span has been strengthened and by-passed.

Iowa. The 11 bridges here are conveniently ranged near State Route 92, which runs across the southerly third of the state. The near-flat roofs on spans around Winterset are especially noteworthy. The Chamber of Commerce in Winterset will send an illustrated map of Madison County covered bridge sites. The Iowa Development Commission (Jewett Building, Des Moines) also has literature.

Kentucky. Has some 25 CB's standing. Contact L. K. Patton, 62 Miami Parkway, Fort Thomas, for latest information. The Department of Public Information (Frankfort) has a pamphlet available.

Louisiana. The one CB here is a privately built structure in East Baton Rouge Parish.

Old double-barreled bridge which once crossed the Sacandaga River at Northampton, N.Y.

Mill Creek Bridge, near Ramseur, N.C., was typical of covered spans in the Old North State.

Private covered bridge over Sinking Creek, near Mountain Lake, Va.

Maine. An important timber-growing state, Maine built a good 120 CB's, has 10 standing today, mostly in the southerly half. Send to the Department of Economic Development (Augusta) for an excellent leaflet locating and picturing them.

Maryland. The seven remaining covered bridges here are located in the northern and central counties. Bunker Hill Bridge, northwest of Hereford, is typical, being newly rebuilt on old plans. Maryland's official highway map spots all sites. Write Department of Economic Development (Annapolis).

Massachusetts. Most of the 10 standing (of more than 100 originally) are in the western half of the Commonwealth. Write the Department of Commerce (150 Causeway Street, Boston) for a CB map. Two active bridge societies (see p. 45) attest to local interest here.

Michigan. Some six bridges remain, in the southern part of the state. The three at Sturgis Lake Dam, Ada, and Greenfield Village (Dearborn) are notable.

Minnesota. The remains of Minnesota's last CB stand in a fairground at Zumbrota, housing a soft-drink and beer concession.

Missouri. Seven bridges still stand on the back roads here, mainly in northern and eastern portions. Best known are bridges near Paris and Burfordville. The Division of Resources and Development (Jefferson City) can provide a list.

New Hampshire. Some 60 bridges, of the 200 or so built, survive, scattered throughout the state. Notable are the outstanding Cornish-Windsor bridge across the Connecticut, the old railroad CB at Bennington, and concentrations of CB's south of Keene and in the Conway region. The New Hampshire Division of Economic Development (Concord) publishes an excellent CB brochure, available on request, and CB's are spotted on the state map.

New Jersey. A restored bridge near Sergeantsville in Hunterdon County, and Barclay Farms, a modern and commodious span near Haddonfield, are the two sole examples here.

New York. Some 28 bridges survive of more than 250 built. If possible visit unique North Blenheim bridge on Route 30 in Schoharie County, southwest of Albany. For location of others, refer to *Covered Bridges of the Northeast* listed on p. 48.

North Carolina. By-passed but preserved, CB's here are located near Claremont, and off secondary roads in Randolph County.

Ohio. Once tops in the country, Ohio, with more than 200 CB's standing, is still the leader in the Middle West. Sending 50¢ to the Ohio Historical Society (Ohio State Museum, Columbus) will bring you a map and directions for how to find them. A listing of the state's CB's by county (as of January '63) is available free from the Department of Development (Columbus). The various county engineers will also send marked county maps, for varying fees. Concentrations of CB's are to be found in Ashtabula, Fairfield and Washington counties.

Oregon. This leading CB state of the West has about 90 standing, all west of the Cascade Range, with concentrations in Lane and Linn counties. See *Covered Bridges of the West,* listed on p. 48, for locations.

Pennsylvania. Here the first CB in the United States was built and here, appropriately enough, most survive (some 300 out of a total of perhaps 1500 built), mainly in the southern part of the state. Concentrations are to be found in Lancaster, Columbia, Washington, and Greene counties. The State Department of Commerce (Harrisburg) has literature available and the Theodore Burr CB Society (see below) sells up-to-date marked county maps.

South Carolina. Three covered spans are all that remain: Chapman's Bridge in Pickens County, Prather's Bridge in Oconee County, and the Long Cane Church Bridge in McCormick County. Further bridge information is available from the State Development Board (Box 927, Columbia).

Tennessee. Half a dozen bridges remain, best known being the Doe River Bridge at Elizabethton. Write Department of Conservation (Nashville) for further information.

Vermont. Nearly 110 bridges, of more than 500 originally, survive, well. distributed in all but one of the state's 14 counties. Big, unique RR bridges are to be found on the line of the St. Johnsbury & Lamoille County RR in the north. Also notable are double-barreled bridges at Shelburne and Middlebury. The Department of Development (Montpelier) will send an interesting map on request.

Virginia. About nine CB's survive, and a leaflet describing them is available from the Department of Highways Information Office (Richmond). Old Humpback, three miles west of Covington, near present U.S. Route 60, is outstanding.

Washington. Two highway and six Howe-truss RR spans remain, all in the coastal region. The longest U.S. surviving railroad CB (450 feet) is near Monroe. Unusual RR-turned-highway bridge is outside of Welcome.

West Virginia. Has better than 30 CB's remaining, with Harrison County, in the north, having the most. The double-barreled Philippi Bridge over Tygart's Valley River is outstanding and historically important as the scene of the Civil War's first land battle.

Wisconsin. A single CB, by-passed and preserved, stands near Cedarburg, north of Milwaukee.

CANADA

New Brunswick. The Howe-truss bridges of New Brunswick, which probably number close to 170 today, make this one of the two important CB provinces of Canada. The bridges are fast disappearing, however. Outstanding is Hartland Bridge over the St. John River, longest in the world. A helpful booklet is available from the N. B. Travel Bureau (Fredericton).

The last of Wernwag's bridges, this fine Erwin, W. Va., span survived Civil War action only to fall 100 years later in a fire set by picnickers.

Only CB left in Wisconsin is this Cedarburg veteran, now by-passed and carefully preserved.

Nova Scotia. Kennetcook in Hants County boasts a single-span CB, sole example in the province.

Ontario. One by-passed bridge survives, spanning Grand River at West Montrose, near Kitchener.

Quebec. Official sources give 246 covered bridges remaining out of a once still-larger number. Road "improvements" are fast reducing this total. For further information and a brochure, write the Tourist Branch (12 Rue Sainte-Anne, Quebec City).

Many housed timber trusses stand today only because the bridges' neighbors and other preservation and history-minded people in the area have taken an active part in seeing that they do survive. Many of these public-spirited individuals belong to one or more of the several societies in America devoted to encouraging interest in, and preserving, covered bridges. Their total membership is now pushing 2000. These groups all publish worthwhile periodicals about covered bridges.

If you are interested in pursuing the subject, why don't you get in touch with one of them?

CONNECTICUT RIVER VALLEY COVERED BRIDGE SOCIETY, care Mrs. O. H. Lincoln, 163 Davis Street, Greenfield, Mass. 01301. Annual membership is $2, plus $1 for quarterly *Bulletin*. Also publishes monthly newsletter, occasional extra bridge lists. Sponsors occasional summer tours; non-members welcome.

INDIANA COVERED BRIDGE SOCIETY, care George E. Gould, 19 Waldron St., West Lafayette, Ind. 61449, or Claude Remaly, Box 198, Rossville, Ind. 46065. Annual membership of $2 includes quarterly *Newsletter*. Also publishes maps locating the state's bridges.

KENTUCKY COVERED BRIDGE ASSOCIATION, care Paul L. Atkinson, P.O. Box 100, Newport, Ky. 41072. Annual membership of $2 includes quarterly *Timbered Tunnel Talk*. Also publishes CB lists, color postcards, notepaper, Christmas cards. Sponsors Annual Bridge Festival in summer; non-members welcome.

NATIONAL SOCIETY FOR THE PRESERVATION OF COVERED BRIDGES, INC., 18 Hillcrest St., Arlington, Mass. 02174; or 272 Main Street, West Acton, Mass. 01780. Annual membership fee of $2 includes monthly bulletins but not quarterly *Covered Bridge Topics* ($1.50 extra). Also publishes *World Guide to Covered Bridges* (see p. 48). Sponsors many summer excursions (write Mrs. Richard P. Bonney, 63 Vermont Street, West Roxbury, Mass., for dates, etc.); non-members welcome.

NORTHERN OHIO COVERED BRIDGE SOCIETY, care Thomas W. Bode, 3254 Crickett Drive, Youngstown, Ohio 44511. Annual membership of $3 for individual, $4 for couple, includes quarterly *Bridge Briefs,* also available to non-members for $1. Runs occasional spring and summer excursions; non-members welcome.

Ontario's sole covered bridge crosses Grand River at West Montrose.

Salt Creek Bridge in Muskingum County before (left) *and after attention from the Southern Ohio Covered Bridge Society.*

SOUTHERN OHIO COVERED BRIDGE ASSOCIATION, INC., care Mrs. Karl K. Knight, 534 Taylor Street, Zanesville, Ohio 43705. Annual $2 membership includes quarterly *Covered Bridge Chatter*. Also publishes tour guides. Occasional tours are sponsored; non-members welcome.

THEODORE BURR COVERED BRIDGE SOCIETY OF PENNSYLVANIA, INC., care Mrs. Vera H. Wagner, 235 Boas Street, Harrisburg, Penna. 17102. Individual membership is $3, couple $5, organization $10, and junior $1. Quarterly *Portals* is sent at no further cost to all except junior members. Runs "See Pennsylvania's Covered Bridges" third week of September annually, also occasional tours in summer and fall; non-members welcome.

ZUMBROTA COVERED BRIDGE SOCIETY, Zumbrota, Minn., was recently formed to care for Minnesota's lone covered bridge. Further information available by writing Box 394, Zumbrota, Minn. 55992.

If You Want to Dig Deeper

IN THE PAST TWENTY YEARS there have been a number of books and pamphlets published on the subject of covered bridges. Here are some of the better and more useful ones, those still in print indicated by an asterisk. The Book Cellar (Brattleboro, Vt., retailer) specializes in this field and will be glad to fill orders.

THE ARCHITECTURE OF BRIDGES by Elizabeth B. Mock, New York, 1949.

A fresh treatment of bridges, heartily recommended.

BRIDGES AND THEIR BUILDERS by David B. Steinman and Sara Ruth Watson, New York, 1957.

A useful general history.*

BRIDGES IN HISTORY AND LEGEND by Wilbur J. Watson and Sara Ruth Watson, Cleveland, 1937.

Cultural history of bridges.

A CENTURY OF OREGON COVERED BRIDGES, 1851-1952 by Lee H. Nelson, Portland, 1960.

State CB history at its best.*

CONNECTICUT'S OLD TIMBERED CROSSINGS by Michael C. DeVito, Warehouse Point, Conn., 1964.

Highly illustrated state rundown.*

THE COVERED BRIDGE by Herbert Wheaton Congdon with photographs by Edmund Homer Royce, Middlebury, Vt., 1959.

Although dated (the book first appeared in 1941), this is a readable story of CB's in general, Vermont's in particular.*

COVERED BRIDGES IN ILLINOIS, IOWA AND WISCONSIN by Leslie C. Swanson, Moline, 1960.

Brief illustrated rundown of bridges in the three states, with maps.*

COVERED BRIDGES OF PENNSYLVANIA DUTCHLAND by Elmer L. Smith with photographs by Mel Horst, Akron, Penna., 1960.

Illustrated pamphlet of CB's in the Keystone State.*

COVERED BRIDGES OF THE MIDDLE ATLANTIC STATES by Richard Sanders Allen, Brattleboro, Vt., 1959.

Essential history and reference for CB's in Delaware, Maryland, Pennsylvania, Virginia, West Virginia and D.C.*

COVERED BRIDGES OF THE NORTHEAST by Richard Sanders Allen, Brattleboro, Vt., 1957.

Basic history and reference for New York, New Jersey and New England CB's.*

COVERED BRIDGES OF THE WEST by Kramer A. Adams, Berkeley, 1963.

CB's in California, Oregon and Washington, past and present.*

WORLD GUIDE TO COVERED BRIDGES, 1959 edition edited by Betsy and Philip Clough; revised 1965 by Harold F. Eastman, National Society for the Preservation of Covered Bridges, Inc., Arlington, Mass.

Handy checklist for locating standing bridges.*

A most useful source of information are the regular publications of the covered bridge societies, which are listed on pp. 45 and 46.

Century-old view of Chicago & Rock Island RR bridge near Colona, Ill.

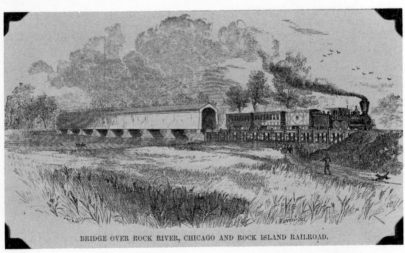

BRIDGE OVER ROCK RIVER, CHICAGO AND ROCK ISLAND RAILROAD.